THE MYSTERY OF

POETRY

NEW GENERATION

Volume I

Cedric D. Harris

THE MYSTERY OF

POETRY

NEW GENERATION

Volume I

Cedric D. Harris

They Mystery of Poetry New Organization

Petersburg, VA

Printed in the United States of America

First Printing, 2019

ISBN 978-0-578-222-89-9

Library of Congress #: 2019910376

P.O. Box 342
Colonial Heights, VA 23803

Dedication Page

Thank God for my mother, Gwen Henderson, my friends and family, including the Harris, Pettaway, Henderson, Epps and Jones families. Also, to my homie, Errol Layne and my sister in the Lord Tabitha, as well as my cousin Janel and anyone who I have been close to. Nobody is a stranger in life, and family is strength. Amen.

CONTENTS

A FLAT TIRE WAS ANOTHER DAY'S COFFEE

A flat tire was another day's coffee.
Wow! On a Monday morning, 11:00 am I was not expecting this to happen during my time of making a move to my next journey, but hey, this is how life is!

It's just another day of a nice, sweet blend; a sip of cream and sugar to make my heart warm up until the time come. I was able to wait for at least thirty minutes for I received help concerning my flat moment, Hey, it was just another day to say, "Another day coffee just waiting for me."

I was going to think of an inspiring time to understand this story. I started writing this in my mind. How I was going to think of a poem in this story? So I decided to write it down as you can see that life is good no matter how flat you become at times because you always get into a place to say, "Hey I will not let anything play with my mind about the good life."

I know, because life is not only what you make it to be, but it's the understanding of how you think in a faith in your belief. So, looks like I needed a cup of coffee in the midst of my thoughts, I carry what another blend in my skull, where the relaxation to my soul, feeling the deepest life inspirational time of my life.

Life is good thoughts, and it's how you believe in your own personal life, because life is not always flat when you take the time to think about another way of getting the right coffee in your soul.

1

Sometimes we only see life from what we naturally see, but if we believe in the faith, then confidence was the key for me. I could not live with believing within my inner self and the life I'm Speaking in the wisdom of my belief, that my life is not flat as some people naturally see me because of this flat tire I had on Monday. As long as my coffee is right and blended with the cream and sugar, I know everything is alright because my coffee was not flat even though my tire was.

Get the clues that I speak, it's the wisdom on the inside from speaking life within me. If someone doesn't understand me, then my coffee understands me because its hot, not cold. So, I'll take the sip again because the waiter was nice enough to me. I'll never have cold feet so, this coffee received me in the heart feeling,

It's was just a good life of drinking coffee and not flat and bitterness.
But a sweet life taste of another day coffee

A LONG WAY FROM TREASURE ISLAND

A long way, oh what a long way, from finding a long way, what a long way!
How long does this take, for I have traveled from far away.

From the countryside, how can I find such wisdom from here? What a long way! What a long way! So how long does this have to take for me to get to the island, for it's too cold in the wilderness. Oh God, this is such a long walk from here! I heard one word speak to me, seek for me, seek for me! I heard the voice say

"Seek for me, search and understand Wisdom. You're still finding out how long is your journey. For where is your faith in me? Do you even see the steps? I've strengthened you inside."

The Lord spoke to me, and I said,
" Lord your faith is in me, ye indeed, so I won't complain about how long is this journey is I will keep walking along the bridge as you guide me along to find Treasure Island."

My faith is the key so I don't need to lose this key, because if I lose my faith then, I will not be able to find Treasure Island, for Wisdom is there. So, I Am going to trust in God that I will catch on to my faith and find Wisdom this time without losing it.

So, I am going to keep on walking and if I fall a few times I will get up again and keep moving I must find Treasure Island.

ANOTHER ANCIENT DAY WAS A LETTER TO GOD

The time in the old ancient times, God was so deep in the center of everything!

Can anybody imagine such understanding?
God Spirit…And how His presence was a masterpiece in the earth and wells the heavens.
Only He declares all the ancient history that no mankind was able to complete.

The mysteries I am writing is the deepest of the heart to toward Him

And the belief in who I am seeking because the One who has no age

The One who is more than I am! My mind couldn't even be transformed

If it was not for the King, oh dear King, I write this letter to thee.

For I know that the world has changed, but you have not changed, because you're the same One who slayed your enemies from long ago, and the ones who were against thee, how great is thy wisdom above fine jewels, yea above fine gold!

Oh Father, in spite of my ways, I am here pressing toward the next mission you have chosen me in this new generation of times! Wow! It's been a thousand years! Such time has been different from the earth days, but I will not forget the days of old times.

THE BATTLEFIELD IS IN THE MIND

The Battlefield is in the mind. At the very serious moment, have you ever understood what is in your head? Early in the morning, your mind begins to function in a very powerful way. Sounds like someone supernaturally is preparing you for the rest of the day, feeling the thunder, in your head waking your spirit so you can be prepared for battle. I see God is strengthening you so much, again from those attacks you're facing; trials and tribulations in your brain cells. But I believe you're able to be free from the weapons of the warfare. It was not carnality to pull you away from standing! Hey, you're a soldier on command!

You're not here to quit this time, because it's a test in the field and the armor of God is in you.

From standing in the battle of your fear, all you have to do is speak the power, and fear will vanish away from you! It's up to you because this is the time for you to face your own opponent by having the courage to face fear again. That's what God is preparing you for every time he wakes you up, showing Glory and power all the time. Each time you awaken, it's preparation and it starts in your mind! Increase function without getting stressed out, for you can't defeat fear by doubting or being scared, just remember the power of speaking life is inside you…think about who is inside of you!

And not just what's only in your head, because the mind is a terrible thing to waste. You're quitting on God and the people you care about, for there are different types of battles.

Your faith is moved by God and turning fears around, gripping on power over! Moving fear, studying yourself, see the wisdom and how you can accomplish more by the way you think. Speak life is life speaking what you believe more than what's in your mind, but in your heart will affect the whole body.

Hey! Don't give up soldier. The battle is not given to you for weakness, but it's for your strength in God.
We have the power to stand my friend wisdom has not given up on you.

DEAR GRANDMA

Dear Grandma, from 1955 it's been a long journey and a long way from home.

It's been a long time from struggling through, what a long way from you!

I see a white blanket in the midst of me.

It appears to be a bright cloth from the rising of the "Sunshine" to see, as I think of someone

Who's been around from ages before me.

I saw grandma in my dream and the family from a long time ago.

It's been a thousand years up in the skies and 2014, all of a sudden, I'm in a journey of seeing the old

cross my path to always remember them who came before I was born. It's back to the future of old.

I've never seen all my family because I was not in existence in those times.

But now since I am here, I am grateful to think about the family that went through a whole lot from a
long time ago, facing the struggles and seeing the future which holds a piece of
grandma that I will not forget.

DEAR GRANDMA

Oh Grandma, I will see you again. Sweet heavenly memory that brings the mystery that lines through the blood line.

The ground gets deep and the winds still blow, the nature still moves, and the grass is steady.

God still remembers them from the days of old. I am seeing the past right before my eyes and understanding the strength of what grandma went through. Dear Grandma, I see the light, oh dear Grandma, I remember the moon light, oh dear Grandma, what a silent night, that screams out in the day.

I saw the old rising from the graves and the seasons have changed, the olden days are remembered.

I feel like Beethoven in a deep mystery as I walk in a dream from the past life. I am the New Creation.

Seeing the past was so real before my eyes and the heritage has made them become history as I am today. I am history, yet though there are many that have a history, but some don't know the inner spirit that you have inside, while writing this mystery, about you dear Grandma, I do remember you.

I am alive to go back in time to think of a forever memory of my grandmother in 1955.

Oh heavens, I am looking forward to seeing you open some day with all of the memories of all races who struggled in those times…

I won't forget Dear Grandma.

FINDING GOOD OUT OF EVIL

Once upon a time in the late 1900's, there was a very strange man named Nicodemus. He lived in a very cold, dark world and he was very lost and could not find the book of God to find His life and how He can be saved from himself, from the evil that lies within his mind. Nicodemus never really understand about life at all. What a cold cave in the dark and lonely night!

And no other life on earth can see him but the shadows of the underworld where he battles against the demons who set him up for the wrong life and how they betrayed him. For so long the demons told him "There was no life for you Nicodemus and no hope for you. Why try to run away from us when you belong down here for there is no life at all for you but the death and the shadow!" But Nicodemus decided to find some confidence and took his time to step out of evil and search for the power to receive the good, for He knew there was someone chasing him in the dark storm.

And for some reason, the other demons were very quiet, but cunning and they did not like Nicodemus because he started to begin his journey to find God in a very deep life! For someone was chasing him for a long time in the night, while the other demons were so busy doubting God and talking about Nicodemus, he was being chased to a long journey in his life. He started to think about life…of how to overcome evil with good and how to fight evil underneath! "Can I be set free?" Nicodemus said unto the LORD! "Please redeem me from evil, dear Lord for I believe in your good." Nicodemus! And God replied unto Him speaking in the silence of rain. Sound deepest in Nicodemus' thoughts to hear God for the first time.

Being chased by God in the middle of the shadow of the night, to find his way to life. So, he took another move and found that God was never dead! He was chasing Nicodemus even while he was asleep, so he had that chance to change his evil to understand the power from heaven to live. Chasing out of death by finding God. Nicodemus searched his way to life! He knew that he couldn't live without God, so He saw a better treasure in his life. One of fighting out from evil ways and fighting well to sustain. There were two parts to Nicodemus; one part of evil, but another part of him was good.

The finding of his evil thoughts was the fight out to study his ways as breath for the first time from ancient of his ages again. He found out that God was not dead, for Nicodemus found favor with good and that was God that gave him life to live.

WE FOUND HOPEWELL

Once upon a time, there was a people from old ages who were gone for thousands of years. So long that not even the new age has heard from them for decades. Some people in the new generation, do not know that the dead are there. Some people don't understand that the unknown is there.

Could they be waiting for the coming, or do they know that the times are changed? For what is dead or who was, is actually alive! These are the days of old and the time has come, that we found Hopewell!

The old has not disappeared but is waiting until it is time for preparation. Indeed, truly the dead will rise again and the those who remain will see the glow from the could the second time.

Nobody knows the time at all, for we are waiting. It's been thousands of years, but there is hope in the well! Can we see the ones who are awakened out of their sleep? Oh yes indeed! Can they understand that there is no fear from the things they've seen or the things they 've heard? Breeze what a drop of sound by the James River and a sound from the center of my chair, I've seen a peaceful moving inside of me while I am thinking, such a mystery! We found Hopewell for thousands of years, while some are sleeping and some are awake, some are shouting and some are silent, but the day will come when we will be together, for there was hope in the well. There was a voice deeper than water and shaking the river like the earth is getting restored from above, what a story of believing in such an interesting chair above this tree that was uplifting my spirit inside of me. I hear a humble voice said to me, "Who was unseen? I saw your faith indeed." He saw my faith immediately. Hopewell indeed.

GOD IN THE MIDST OF FOG

Man! Who gave a blessing back to God in the midst of fog? One step away from the wilderness, I'm in war; one step away from lack and another step away from the creeping thing that tries to pull me away from a blessing! I must give back to bless God.

So hey, you can't fog! It's no way you can't blind my eyes from seeing my way through! Oh no you don't! I will beat you with the sound of the Word.

When I speak life, may the wind I hear! Push the fogs away so I can be guided along the way, its goose bumps touching my skin, but my heart is increasing the kindle of flame in the midst of troubles, I will bless God. It's a loop in life, in the earth feels like I'm rumbling. Hey, what a candle I have in my battles! Could this be a test of my faith to receive my mantle? Through it all I am facing obstacles…fogs…but I leap over a wall out of these fogs that wrestle against my call! Hey everything looks to fogging over here.

Oh Lord, could this be hard for me to comprehend my thinking? A foggy mind can be the deep cloud to challenge my faith. Wait a minute, I am hearing a sound system coming from the rock of the ancient days.

I must take this step further up. What a dream out of I see out of my desert places. What a move I feel from the rock of days! In the midst of time changes, I give a blessing back to God in the midst of fogs from a stormy cold night, I feel the light kindle my heart, it was the purpose I gave a blessing heart back to God in the midst of fogs.

The Lord said unto me, "Young man, it's not for you to know what happened before time. Just go hard after me and I will mold you far above rubies since you gave your heart to me, the wisdom has fallen inside of you because of me, so don't worry about troubles in the land, keep the faith and watch and pray."

Former things have appeared before your eyes today. From the blessing from God, any person who gave God their heart has blessed God In the midst of fogs. Even a blind man can sense the move of God within the inner self that sees God, but the outward appearance is a test of your faith.

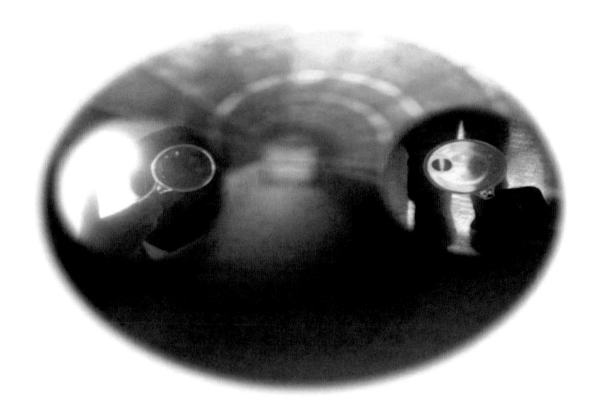

HAS ANYBODY SEEN GOD

HAS ANYBODY SEEN GOD? Does anybody know the truth? There are many viewers but not understanding the clues in life. Could there be some outsiders that no one has not seen in the planet?

Hey, I know we are not the only ones breathing in the earth world. Does anybody see the turn around and the shifting in the worlds? Hey, do you see that this world is not turning on its own?

Do you understanding we have not created ourselves? Do you see confidence? Because I'm beginning to find life somewhere. I notice from waking out of a dream, yet though there are many dreams I've experienced while living on planet earth when I fall asleep at night, of course it's a whole another world out there!

As we see within ourselves, there is someone breathing and someone protecting and progressing within us because the breath we breathe is not working alone. There's no way we can live without breath in our lungs. So, hey have you seen confidence? Because we will find some results.

Because so many people are wondering about God. Some say, "I heard of Him" or "I know Him" or who is "Him". But the picture is, do we know and understand anything about Him, or do we only see Him in the image of something or someone in the figure of frame? Hey, does anyone ever think about who framed GOD?

Hey, truth be told, of course God is not mocked and not only is God invisible and no man has seen God at any time and we not only think before we speak, but we give a faith answer on what's our true belief.

17

Do we believe in Elohim or not? He is the invisible One that lives in us! What's going on? I feel a heartbeat. Where is this heart coming from and what is that noise up ahead? Let go see what's happening.

As we go across this bridge tunnel, let's see what lies ahead so believe it or not pal, have you find results about this story I'm refreshing to you? Or do you think this is some gimmick or are you only seeing what your mind tells you to believe? Or do you have the power to believe who was really inside you?

In our next chapter we will travel to another dimension…

I FINALLY FOUND WISDOM

Wow was a very long way from home, so far away from home! It's been a long trip from home, and a long journey to me. Well looks like I finally found wisdom indeed for I had a long time searching.

For years after years gone by and I finally see that wisdom was from above indeed for even though I had a hard time finding and even asking around where I could find thee in the middle of all the struggles I had appeared to see! Oh Lord how great is this? To be I see that wisdom was from you indeed and I Had

A hard time in life and a huge battle with the enemy, for he was trying to fight against my spirit so I had to keep on moving and focus straight, then I was able to see that wisdom was not from any creature on the planet but it was from above.

I believe that my request was made known unto thee, Oh Lord, there nothing can be compared unto thee and in the evening times and the night season was some ways rough for me that I could hardly sleep. It was so much dream alerts in my rest and so much violence

On planet earth so I had to look straight and press towards wisdom and it was very pleasant that I had help along this journey, in my life. Thank God for the hidden spirit man who guides such a clay like me.

I FINALLY FOUND WISDOM

To understand wisdom is the key to my energy and greater than any other things for wisdom you are the tree that brings such growth in my life and I am glad to see that you are the tree that sits strong.

Just like the blazing of fire in my walkway while I seek after such a mystery to see that wisdom the burning tree lives and very consuming to be in part of me while I seek thee in the middle of struggles.

I am glad that you're still teaching me patience and helping my heart each time I use my faith, that I finally found the wisdom tree. And breaking out of bondage to be free!

In faith we believe wisdom is the Spirit of God well human beings can succeed indeed.

POEM OF WISDOM

For a long time, it's been so long in this life, and times are flying by. Many times, I have been searching for the wisdom I need, has anybody seen wisdom? And where is the key or who is the key to understanding?

I remember a story from a man name Solomon, He was such a strong man of God. Even though he had five wives and five concubine's, but the good news is he decided that having all the goods in the land and plenty of women he thought was his desire in his life, but someone was calling him for a serious person in his life, and the voice was so deep that His words shook the heavens and earth and everything that dwells therein. Such a sound that sounds like a strong voice of thunder, and king Solomon knew that the voice caught his attention and the sound of heaven that He felt God tugging his heart.

So, he took the time to find his purpose in His life and wisdom was the answer in the king's heart. One thing about God, he understood that it takes a little king's heart to give it to such a great and merciful God who sits above His throne. The key was the voice from the king saying, "I need wisdom where can I find such wisdom dear Lord?"

Well I understand that in the old testament, the king found his wisdom. Now in the new age I am living in, what a new dimension I am in! What a new dream I see, and what a book I am seeking for and the power that fills my motions streams. I have a long walk up these stairs, but something is in front of me that is challenging me and blocking me to get through and I see the only way I can get through is to find the key to my understanding. This is a long journey for me, in the year of 2014 December the eighteenth, I'm still alive! Through my stumble and falls, I was almost taken and now since I have a long journey from home, such a faraway country, I still have to unleash the right key concerning wisdom. Let's see here, ok, King Solomon received wisdom. Well so can I! Looks like I need to press my way up these long stairs, yes indeed, I will not give up on finding the book of wisdom of God.

WRITTEN MYSTERY

Love from the sky to the ground

Love from the sky to the ground is there true love around?

Is fear trying to take me down? Why does it seem like I'm so alone in the dark? Who can exchange my heart to feel I am needed? Does anybody really love me? Why do I get tired of feeling this way? I don't want to be alone too long, for I understand that God said He will never leave me neither will He forsake me, so why do I feel so alone in the world at times?

I feel like I'm just by myself and getting upset over this. Is there love from the sky to the ground? Hey! Who is touching my eyes from all these lonely nights I've cried myself to sleep? O Lord could that be you quietly coming to visit a troubled person like me? I don't want to let my heart be the problem, so Lord I give them all to you because the power you shared towards me, I now see that I am not alone. So yes, I believe there is love from sky to the ground for me! I am welcome to the planet and believing I am love, with no fear holding me. I am free in my mind, and I exchange my lonely nights into a candle lit dinner for the one you created me to be…beautifully and wonderfully well-made!

I am the love from the ground, the rose for you. Lord your grace as open heaven loved. And forgiveness has received me because your power showed me how to love unconditionally. My spirit is willing even though my flesh is weak…but my spirit is willing. I am encouraging one heart to have strong love for thee. I am sky free to give my heart away to your love, compassionate on you to me. I will not hold no grudges from my past because my dreams are in front of me. I am love so you did set me free to enlighten my destiny. So, I dry my tears and will walk and live strong without wavering

So "YES!" to love! This is why my ground is free. Shiny rose!

STRENGTH BEYOND THE PAST

Oh, I Need Strength right away! Oh My God what is happening to me? I've had so many different changes in my head lately, to the point I could not comprehend anything! Something is tackling my mind.

Dwelling on the past is my headache, like a hot tomato sauce in a frying pan. I need power over the past.

So, I'll just write the vision in the future instead, what a struggle in my thoughts! I'm shaking like I feel the wrong vibe trying to pull me away from writing! Oh no you don't devil! You are not going to take my future! You better think again!

I know I could have left God a long time ago, even though I ran away seventy times seven, looking distressed, when the whole time my closet was a mess. I could not focus on nobody else but my walk through this map quest, in my brain, there must be a strong sound, deeply telling me, "Write the vision down and make it plain", and I understood that voice, but after a while my strength been weak through the past crazy relationships that were not really meant for me. Dang! What the world? Is this past still wrestling me in my room? Away from my sheets, you old self! For the past was gone! And you're still trying to come again?! Real talk, my strength is beyond the past, while I'm writing inside the future.

I know believers say, "If you resist the devil, he shall flee", but dear Lord please forgive me because I have not always followed along with your Word speaking to me. Truth is, I was battling in the sheets like it was an ugly creep hindering me in my sheets. So, I had to bind the enemy again and even pouring blessed oil over my room, with a stretched out arm and a heart that beats so strong. As I listen to the voice who said, "You will be strong, even while your weak! But my love is made perfect through it all. But whatever you do! Just don't walk away from me." The Lord told me to straighten up for there is a purpose in your life. Be free, the past was done, so now I am present and the future I was holding. The Lord said to me!

The future I saw was not my own, never really understood, nothing much up ahead. If I can write inside the future, I believe the word instead. While it looks like I see a night vision of blood written in red.

The one who is above everything indeed! I see a new generation functioning in the future.

THE CLAY MAN RUNNING

Clay man running so fast trying to be strong!
But sometimes he was weak facing trial and tribulations and was ready to give up. Too many hurts from the past was his problem. He didn't know how to overcome much, so he went to many different people and tried to get prayer and too many of the battles he had was not quite fair.
He was ready to quit on God once, but he knew that he just couldn't give up on himself.

So, he ran as fast as he could to understand who is best for him and understood there was a dream he was seeing! "Oh building! Oh buildings! When are we going to be compacted together?

Why are you so worried about yourself? Don't give up on the purpose that God has for you. Truly God didn't allow Clay Man to give up at all! Looks like he had been doing some thinking because he remembered who saved him from the wooden cross! The brother had serious work to do, so he knew he needed to be constructed by someone greater that himself, and that name was the God of Abraham the God of Isaac and the God of Jacob, the Lord of Hosts is His name!

So, hey Mr. Clay man, you've got work to do, because you're a part of God masterpiece, a of work of art! The building and the rest of the buildings of those who received the Lord God all mighty because many buildings need work. Some are stronger than others and some are halfway, and some are straightened, and some are broken but needs to be fixed!

Well what a journey this is to be with God in the land of the living!

So many times, we see lots of things going on, but we can't put our focus on that. We must put our hands to the plow. That's it! Yeah, hands to the plow! Hmm…sounds interesting! There are more things happening in the planet earth, and new things every day! Especially new creatures are coming, we just don't know, but we can understand that each day seems like one minute rain, one minute snow, and one minute sun comes out, and hey one word is good enough to keep us that's for sure! This is a great, deep journey to believe God through the ups and downs but check this out! OK, looks good, understanding this deep walk is to have a gentle relationship with the Father

THE VIRTUOUS WOMAN

Once upon a time, as I Cedric was traveling down the highway, I suddenly ran into one of my sisters in Christ who was facing storms and fighting to survive through hard times in life. One day we finally bumped into each other and I saw her praise dancing before God, then I saw how virtuous she has become in her testimony called, "Out with the old and in with the new".

As I was seeing the test she was facing, I knew right then and there it was time to help a sister; paint an old house that she used to live in and I tell you she was very quietly humble, praying in every area of her life. My brother in the Lord, Errol and I decided to pull together and help her paint, for it was time for a serious paint job. Wow! It was hours even until a few days, but through it all we were able to pull together and the good news is that we help build each other faith.

God definitely saw her faith and to see the virtuous woman she has become; brilliant in her walk with God. One late night, she went into the other room and had a thought about one night with the King who is over everything, suddenly there was a shining light flashing before her eyes.

She began to look outside and saw the glory in the midst of her and she went outside like it was a beautiful feeling to be in the presence of God in her life, then she was listening to a soft sound.

Her heart started to beep, beep, beep, and sound like music in her spirit in thinking of a song of praise and the holy spirit begin to anoint her mind and begin to say, "Oh daughter, Oh daughter, your faith has moved me in your life and your two brothers in Christ. Even though you three were tired, I have strengthened the knees, for I will bless thee above measure and bless your children indeed. You are virtuous above rubies. Indeed, you have succeeded, for you are a virtuous woman and anyone who seeks God with a pure heart will be virtuous. Every struggle is a testimony and the reward is plentiful from heaven." For the glory of God's eyes was too holy for her to look upon, He blessed her provision.

WISDOM THOUGHTS

1. Use wisdom instead of fighting fire with fire, without spoiling your way to be successful at any Perseverance in business; without fighting fire with fire but be strengthened in your accomplishments because every test happens. But using wisdom makes room for a successful career and respect with others no matter what issue you're facing. Be humble…be strong.

2. We must make sure when we are speaking by facts and not just by the other's opinions at business. So even if he or she has their points across, the first thing is to listen, then speak without always being outspoken or assuming about the person's answer. Learn to be wise, take counsel with each other, with reason and respect one another without wrestling with the problems in whatever statement comes across, just take a good challenge and you both solve the solution without arguing over it. Solve it together, that's how you build an organization with wisdom starts now.

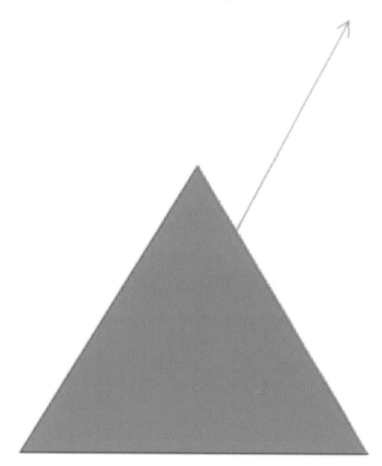

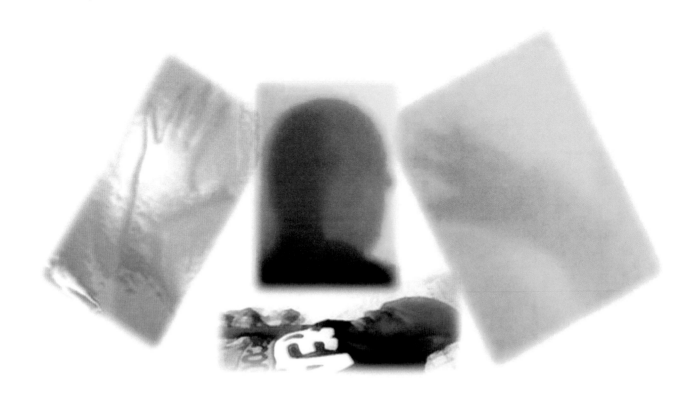

RESURRECTED DREAMS

Resurrected dreams. I am thinking of the goodness of the King who never quit on a child of God that desires to go forth and excel in his dreams! To understand the storms was not to take him away from pressing towards the life that he brings the best into his visions of everything of course.

God is the one who knows how to set up things. Why do battles in life get in the way of brothers and sisters in this reality! Oh, I see! It's only a test really, because no matter what life brings, our dreams are still alive, so we don't have to waver around doing the same old thing!

Let's see, how about some beautiful sounds of the piano playing in the backyard of my mind? Wow! I'm thinking melody sweet. I don't need to eat up hot tamales that will put spice to my teeth. Hey, our dreams are alive while we face the former things. The storm is in our way, but our hearts are available to the Lord God in the midst of all things!

Of course, I have a thinking cap, and resting like the One who taught me patience, only He has His way of doing things. Beep! Beep! My heart is singing a meditation song! I'm letting my ears do the time and the word moves inside, listen ok? Our dreams never have to die, but the sky does rewind with the tick tock clock. The brain can function better on the right time, thinking of the living room where God moves. Arise from sleep, thinking about inner man to one part of me is the outside view, but the inner man stays alive like a humble instrument with the soft-hearted sound that gets God's attention. While thinking on Him, while He makes all things new, our dreams are resurrected because Christ is our Lord that gave us dreams to believe He can do the impossible thing! Yes, I think deep, that's why the clock is stopped, because it's my nap time. While I just trust God in everything because He created us by His likeness and purpose so we can dream and be part of God's dream and vision is to stand make moves, have patience while awaking. I am courageous and I see the vision is believing in the faith in how to believe, thinking of the One who was blessed, and quietness and He knew how to show up on the right time.

He is the only way that sustains us today to be the impact dreamers and never losers but humbleness through the stormy, cold winters, never quitters with no more bitters but having faith in God is to believe we are the dreamers!

Like deep thinkers better than a hard bottle of stressful liquor! I rather live like a Dreamer. Our dreams are not dead but alive. OK, peace.

FINDING GOD IN THE MIDDLE OF ARMAGEDDON

There is more than what we think and what we say there's more than what we know than some people really believe. Some say there are no aliens at all, but honestly, they don't see real close. There is most definitely another world out of space, believe it or not. One day I went outside at night flashing my iPhone around and I saw the reflecting of the light bulb while I waved my phone taking pictures. The strangest thing happened! The moon just all of a sudden started peeking! Well of course God created sun and moon I know that but something about the moon it looked like there were eyes up there! It's like I've sense it then I when in the house and plugged my phone up and started looking at the pictures I took and all of a sudden I felt some type of gravity and not only that I felt like someone was watching me the whole time. It felt like my back was touched by an invisible feeling. I was not in fear though, but I see there is a lot more going on to our planet than what we think and what we say and believe, truly there's war coming soon! Just As the bible told us there will be many wars, rumors of war, kingdoms against kingdoms!

The demons are against our Lord Christ and the church, but it's the time for a serious coming together and getting ready for the battle facing the giants, the spirits who have an attack with mankind. Having the powers of deception from the skies, coming against us with many kinds of issues and imaginations trying to tear us apart! Under these demons are our enemies from the very first start-way before Adam and Eve's time-truly the earth was dark before for the devil knows his times are very short so we can't afford to give up now. Salvation running things constantly. Now there is too much trouble in the earth! Too many people killing each other over a whole lot of garbage, fighting over money sex and drugs, killing ourselves! So what we going to do now? Come on! Why fight another man that breathes just like you? You should know already the devil don't like you! Hey, we need to team up salvation army! We need to step up now! If we all come together, the enemy can't mess with us because God is with us! No matter what, we are protected from the devil roaming from mars and earth, now roaming around lurking up and down trying to take a peek at many people to see who he can deceive!

I know that the enemy is the problem with the society. Armageddon is soon to come, but our God and Lord Christ and the CHURCH already Won let's stay prayed up because Armageddon will be done. But because of Christ's Crucifixion over two thousand years ago, it was finished a long time ago. We're also as aliens unto God, because we didn't have a Savior, but now we are no more alienated but dear children of God through Christ Jesus the King of everyone and Lord over the dead and Living creation.

We will not be confused! Even the devil changes himself to an angel of light but he is defeated during THE TIMES OF Armageddon battle! 10-4 roger that!

MENTALLY FREE

Mental freedom, inside and outside. We are off the chain! We are the creation that goes through battles in our minds. BE FREE!

As we see the penguin, having the ability to be strong and the wisdom, who knew what to do with all kinds of things, and feeling like the chain in to be broken is to be freedom. Overcoming the step in life that seems to be worry and fearing, but the key is that I have the strength to keep my heart now! I'm being strong minded.

We can strive just like brothers and sisters in these communities, understand that society is running in many different places. So many times, in life, people have a battle with depression. I know you came become freedom! Think about that, because we have been facing things coming against us in many different places, but real talk nothing, can take us! Down because we are the last days and times, representing the Kingdom of God, we are claiming and aiming to the freedom. The mind is freedom and no chains, no games to the brains, but take out depression and leave fear in the river. Let it float away from these cities and bring the wisdom of coming together building a stable communities truly we are mentally inside and outside freedom as I open my eyes to see looks like freedom and not even after my own ego, but believing that we are unity to be made free.

WE ARE THE TEMPLE

(Inspired by 2 Corinthians 6:16)

Thinking about the Lord who is with us and the holy of holies. Arise to help us! We are the temple of Him who came to Comfort us. Men, women and children! The time is close, and the years are thousands, but the days are at hand. While the waters are still, can we be still to know He is our God of truth as we prepare for Him in understanding? How brilliant wisdom is!

While we dwell in the statutes of the all mighty, inside spirit of truth, I'm thinking of His statues' nourishing good fruits! We feel that His heart is the key that we stand together in the utmost holy faith. In our hearts, we believe in Him who is invisible and makes things possible to us today! For us living in the flesh called the clay.

"O Lord teach us Thy statutes; and we shall live and keep them unto the end of days. Give us understanding, and we shall keep thy law; yea we shall observe it with our whole heart.

Make me to go in the path of thy commandments; for therein do we delight, make us understand the way of thy precepts: so, shall we talk of thy wondrous works for our soul melts for heaviness: strengthen thou us according unto thy word. Remove us from the way of lying, lips and grant us thy law graciously.

We have chosen the way of truth! Thy judgments have laid; before us, O Lord put us not to shame. We will run the way of thy commandments, when thou shall enlarge our hearts. And we shall walk at liberty in thy precepts dear Lord we dwell in the house of the living God, Amen"

WE ARE THE TEMPLE

To the living epistles and to the memories of king David and Moses and Aaron, Joshua and John with Apostle Paul including Peter who was called Cephas, a stone, and our Lord and savior Christ Jesus and his mother Mary with the rest of the men and women who are written in the holy Bible scriptures and us that are stamped in heavenly places through Christ the Son of man that chosen us by God, faithfully as we believe the gospel of Christ to keep Him in remembrance forever. Many are called but few are chosen. Glory to the Holy Spirit who is sincere by His Love and comforter of all and in you all Amen.

And I myself Cedric Harris love you to May God Father bless you in One Love through His Faithful. Be encourage my brothers and sisters I hope you enjoy these inspirational movie poems written by my heart with Courage and integrity of a unique ready

Writer living epistle writer by faith

I also give all my honor and glory to God and the Lord Jesus Christ who blessed me with the preparation

And predestinated me in these last days....

Also I like to thank my mother Overseer pastor Gwen Henderson and founder of the Christian charities of deliverance church and my godfather apostle Norris porter from long island New York, and evangelist Roberts and the mothers the missionaries of the church who encourage me concerning my goals in life, and my aunt Debra and grandmother Vivian Jenkins and the rest of any brothers and sisters who gratefully encourage a brother like me and one of my brothers pastor Allen Rucker who I use to do gospel rap with a while back , God bless you brother man and all and any one from state of Virginia and new Yorkers an Texas and north Carolina from anywhere I thank you very much sincerely.

of a poet in the gospel and I like to thank the rest of families and friends who encourage me as well and I like to thank the Lord for a new chapter in my future a special woman of God! Name Anisha walker has come into my life the woman of God; at the very present time of Valentine season! Here's a quote

* Scriptures referenced: Ps 119:28-35

CAMPING WITH GOD

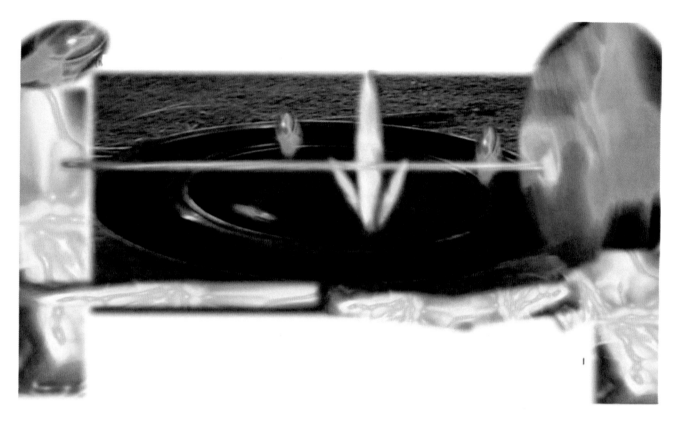

In the midst of my life, because of my belief in Him, blessed are those who believe in God. No matter what, the camp is ready, the fire is blazing, strength is in my wash pot, and this fire never runs out. For this is purifying and each time in the fire is like facing the face of God by the action of my faith.

I'm out camping in the midst, having the words of my mouth with meditation in my spirit, taking the time, being strong in the temple, getting the confidence in the fire that I need from God. For I can't give away my heart to anything that doesn't have the fire blazing. For there is only one who is refreshing and furnishing my spirit, who is truth in my heart, for this temple is His and nothing can take away what He has prepared, for this is my offering-seeking Him face to face from the abundance of my soul!

I saw dreams come true when I speak life and believe God!

I'm out camping with God, in the midst of the fire, and thinking about the blaze of His anointing, coming on to me while I breathe. Strength! For I see the fire blazing in the center of my life,
I SEE THE MOVE OF God

For the enemy could not even get in my vision, for he was not strong enough to take my soul.

My heart was too hot for him. He is nothing but lost! Tossed to and fro! But as I follow the Spirit of Truth, I know I am hot for sure! The One who is more powerful than I, from the depths of my soul, I said "yes". All hail to the master of my soul! Glory to the King who sits upon the throne while I have a good time!

CAMPING WITH GOD

Camping with Him while He sits high and saw me in the blaze while I think of Him on the throne.

I'm shut up in my bones! He never leaves me alone, because He is my strength and great is the campfire.

When I seek His face in the midst of fire, while His glory above my head while ministering and facing the shadow of my soul speaking life. In the midst of fire, my faith has really been hot, so I'll never be cold.

While out camping with God.

ARISE OF THE WARRIORS

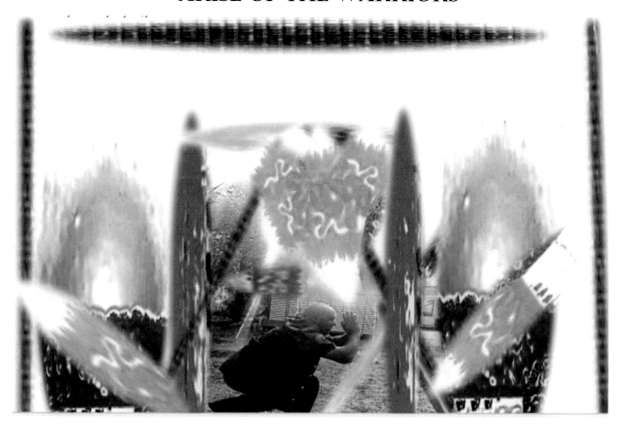

The men Arise out of trouble…Arise out of problems. Take position, Arise Warriors!!!

All men…ARISE out of stress, ARISE out of fear, Arise out of weakness and fight for your rights! Arise out of those things that tried to bring you down, come on! It's time for the uprising of the warriors! Be strengthened in the power of the calling! Let's just strip the enemy out of his power by the words of our mouth! Even as we pray, we speak by our faith unto the rising of our courage! And the battles? We can face them! We will not bow to BAAL or any false god! We will follow the truth of our Lord, just like the Hebrew boys!

We have no time to argue and fight against each other but listen to the Word of God when He said "love one another and strengthen one another and protect the women who are striving alone. Never leave the women behind." So, take the stand and set everything in place. We are men! We shall stand up and be firm and take our places! The devils can't have our places! They can't have our families! We have the power of God's armor on us and only Onc CREATOR who is protecting all of us! We believe we have received Him within us! Yes, He is God and beside Him there is no other! For if God be for us, who can be against us? In our lives and real soon he will put our enemy, the devil, away from telling all kinds of lies; we have a great inheritance my brothers and sisters! No matter what all hail to the King the Lord whose strength is stronger than men who are weak. But in faith, we are strong! The enemy can't have our campfire!

So, remember, Arise men and women! Let's be strong in the earth element!

DEFEATING THE PILLS AND PROTECTING THE WALLS

Protecting your walls...protecting your strength... protecting your mind...is like keeping your walls strong

Enter into the gates of the presence of God, getting the peace you need and not having fear and anxiety that will ruin your needs. The thing we need is the power over fear that torments us mentally. What is our weapon of war and our strength to stand firm, in this warfare? We can't afford to give our strength to the issues that pull our spirits down, we need to keep our guard up. Keep our spirits up and tell the devil to shut up, and take a stand understand the power that you have inside you.

Step out of your comfort zone, get in a place of rescuing you, proceed in those things that bring your life into another atmosphere to pull you away from the best inside you. Get the understanding that God is with you just take the time to say, "I will not let fear pull my mind out of God's inheritance for me or my family. I will not let paranormal attacks hinder my life, for no weapon formed against me or my family shall prosper and any tongue that rise against me they shall be defeated by the one who is above and inside me for I am life!

Speak life, because with these walls up, my mind is blocked from the enemy's attacks!

"I have my war clothes on and no matter how much I fall off, I have the mind of Christ to stand, representing thy Kingdom!

"I will not be defeated, for the only thing I have in mind is that I am free!"

"No chains can't pull my thoughts"

"I have joy over sadness"

"I am at peace, defeating anger."

"I will prosper over poverty."

DEFEATING THE PILLS AND PROTECTING THE WALLS

"I will overcome the things that the enemy will try to do!"

Remember we have destiny, so that is the choice we have to make in our life. Nothing can knock our wall down but us! We have to guard our hearts and minds from all types of weapons that the enemy throws! Put a brake on the issues and start speaking power over your issues!

Protecting your wall is within you! All glory to God that is helping you accomplish your dreams!

To Strengthen the spirit of your mind, from turning and spinning around, wondering why we go through. Just speak life and watch your walls increase wisdom and just watch God move as you move.

Defeat the pills! What are your pills today? Listen, take the time to defeat anything in your mind that is warfare in you. Just remember, praying in the key! And faith will release the door for you as long as you defeat the pills and overcome all types of fears.

HELLO...MY NAME IS FORGIVEN

Hello, my name is <u>Forgiven...</u>

Once upon a time I was falling into sin so much in my life, and I decided to pray, and God reminded me that we all have sinned and come short of His glory.

One Saturday night was a rough night of my life, battling with stuff that can take my thoughts.

And I knew that I just had to pray because I just could not take this anymore in my own life.

Behind closed doors there are battles that anybody faces even in your dreams at night.

When you're asleep, that's when the enemy will try you, but at the same time the flesh is so weak.

But our spirits are better and ready to be willing to get up and pray while the time is day.

Sometimes life can be so clocked up when you're facing so many issues, that it takes a long time to overcome.

But one Sunday morning at one o-clock, God woke me up out of my sleep and told me that

My name is Forgiven. So, I took the time to get up and go to the bathroom, anoint my head and wash my face. Then lighting flashed and hit my faith like rain overflowing through the center of the earth.

I bowed down to God and thanked Him for forgiveness from all of my sins. If anyone fall seventy times seven the Lord is faithful and just to forgive. Hey, my name is Forgiven! And your name is Forgiven!

The past is over unless you're stuck in your past like a clock with no elbows, laugh out loud, understand.

Seek forward towards the future principles. Hey, your past was a message for you to aim into your dreams in a positive way. Anyone has negative ways, but every challenge is a test for us to accomplish.

Whatever we face in life is only a trial of our faith in God, hey I am confident and not forgotten.

You are strong and your life is not settled for disclosure, for every purpose is new every morning.

And every time the sun shines during the day has a time God uses the sun as a clock, in his own watch.

For no one knows His time or His coming because there is nothing new under the sun.

Hey, honestly, I prefer my mind be filled with words from my heart than to have numbers on my back.

For the life I speak is powerful and the life you speak is powerful. Each time you speak into your dreams and believe in what you speak, for one day if the clock stops just know you still can make a move.

By choices, Forgiven is the power over guilt and shame. Forgiveness has no time frame on it. But is forever.

Just don't go back to the same fallen way. Forgiven is in our roots. Love washes us through, Seven is our complete understanding, which came from God giving mankind the wisdom and knowledge to believe in Him.

We are Forgiven and not forbidden. We are Kingdom and not bound by the past. We are the future up under grace.

I AM GRATEFUL

I am grateful to be one of God's children on the planet called earth and I am also grateful that I did not give up and quit on my dreams and the visions that are in store for me.

I'm grateful that my mother beats stroke, for she is a strong healthy mother and my grandmother as well they both almost died from heart issues, but I thank God and am grateful that Christ Jesus is real

And got heart heal a lot of us little people down here in the earth and I am grateful that I can go outside and see nature and live life without complaining but to be grateful for all the things that are good even in the skies and also I am grateful I can go out of my way to help somebody else on this earth.

Because we all need each other, and we can't give up on each other. We must be grateful because there are other places where some people are going through a lot more struggles and hard times and some of us today.

I am grateful that I can share my goods to somebody who is in need and if anything I can do to help I am grateful to do that I believe trees are powerful and grateful to stand firm and I believe a lot of us can trust God and stand as well without quitting especially with school or another dreams.

We are not alone in the world even though sometimes we can get lonely or discouraged, but in the midst of battles and going through, we still have to be grateful in critical issues because it's just a test in life.

I am grateful my faith is steady. It makes me want to sing a rock steady beat song in my head.

Be grateful with the things you are able to do and be happy with yourselves, even if somebody doesn't want to see you make it strong. Just remember, be strong like this tree.

I am grateful I can encourage somebody else from falling away, from facing their fear.

We can overcome our fears if we face them. Be grateful and have gratitude with a great attitude

OK Dude…Peace!

A WALK WITH GOD

I had a deep walk with God on Wednesday, and it's been a journey of my life.

And wow! I was almost gone before along my way home and in the deepest cold dark side.

It was not for me to dwell in the midst of that, because I understood that there is someone who really cares about His creation. I am one of them. For a while I didn't know how to walk right, no joke. Even when I was a little baby boy I could not walk, for I was seriously handicapped. When my mother first had me, I didn't know my legs were not properly straightened.

Hey, this reminds me of how falling into sin will make your life very miserable, to the point it eats you up! And you find out walking backwards was not the right road to take! But great Scott, I am still alive! All because of the grace and mercy of God. He did not leave a soldier left out!

I believe that God saw my faith being very exposed to His eyes. To the point He must be so happy to guide me on the way. He spoke His Word like water pouring flame of a miracle whip in my life as young boy.

So now since I am a man, thank God I can walk, for He healed me! That's for sure! I'm telling you.

We have a serious journey to establish and every journey is very different. It looks like this journey with God is very sensitive in the spirit realm and I see that, and no matter where I go, I will keep the faith and keep it moving. For some reason, I wonder if it's a door I see up ahead. But there's something about this door, it's invisible, with a dove above it I can see. Hmmm, this is very deep. What is this I feel? Woo! What a chill to my heart and what an inner flame in my thoughts! Wow! Are those wings holding up the stairs? For this was from God! What an outstanding demonstration! The stairs look very deep and are a straight path.

So, along this road is going to be something, very modern maybe, but we will see.

Wednesday was a deep walk with God, and I know I have an interesting testimony to share with the world so that somebody can be free.

Well, it's been a pleasure to walk with god again… after all by faith, not sight!

Hey Good news! We are going to make it if we only believe in the word called, John 3:16 is the walk of freedom that ring.

NO EVIL CAN...

New   beginning.   Chapter; Poem-0
(Psalms memory)

No evil can befall thee! No evil can take me down! I am a warrior of the highest God!
I will not fail this quest in my life! I will overcome for I am covered by a mighty strong hand!
All hail to my king!

All hail to the lord whose voice is deeper than many waters, who defeats our enemy and teaches us to
fight and our hands to war! Glory to the One who spoke in psalm 91 to verse ten. Holy is thee who
keeps us dwelling in the secret place, for he is the Most High of all!

Holy Lord God Almighty! The one who defeated Lucifer, called the devil of darkness, the sorcerer the
evil one who is the deceiver. For he is defeated by the Word of truth. Our God is our King who
strengthens us while going through. Our king is the King of kings and Lord of lords, who is MIGHTY to
save, MIGHTY to stand, MIGHTY to help and MIGHTY to deliver all the creation all over the worlds,
from heaven to earth! He who showed us the way, All Hail to the Christ our Lord!

Today…No Evil shall not befall thee! No devil shall defeat thee! No glory to the enemy for
all the Glory belongs to our Lord, our God, our true living King!
Anchor! Anchor! Hear me ROAR!!!

ONE NATION WORLDWIDE PRAYER

One nation worldwide prayer.

In the world people are going through strategies, and in these times, we must pray without doubting.

So, let's grab on the faith we need! Power to the people!

The only way to be redeemed by the power, is to believe in God who is within us by rights and not by works of our own selves. Just by faith, we can fight together. It doesn't matter what race or nationality you are; this is the worldwide prayer of the human rights society is in us. We are experiencing a human life that has a spiritual integrity and due to the fact that we are all colors, we must remember, we have the power over the these we are able to do, but do not have the power to enslave one another

We have the AUTHORITY to grow and work with one another and that's how we built a strong world.

We are the world made by God Himself. So, as I pray today, I will pray for the whole entire world.

As I lift up my hands, I pray you will receive these words today in the faith.

"Dear God, we come together with one accord, we come together in one faith and we pray for all nations and all countries. For we have power over hate and faith over fear, we have power over depression just like power over poverty, same way, power over the false allegation, and power over fate, but love covered all of us because we are the power to the people by rights and freedom, not by laws or the works of men hands. But only in the faith, without faith works are dead, but through faith we have a lively move"

THE COMFORTER

One day, a knock at the door, a voice spoke to me saying, "Fear not for I am with thee and nothing can take you away from me, for I am with you forever. It's been years since I've been in your life. I'm on a mission taking care of all your problems with a comfort, for I am the pillow of life that's been watching over you every time. The door to your destiny is here and as long as you're with me and believe, you will never lose your destiny for dreams do come true! Wow! Thousands of years and you're still looking good. Ever since I kept you from evil, I knew that I had to protect you because of the love in your heart. No fear in me because sacred darling you live."

O Holy Spirit it's been a pleasure!

Do get to know the love you shared in my life for so long, for I have not always been "Mr. Nice Guy", or the good saint, but all I can say is "thank you" for protecting such a soul saved Christian like me.

Through the hours of the night and the day spring, you're there and from dust to dawn you're still watching over me and the whole entire world who believe in you. For everyone has a dream that believes in you and the life they speak and make the move in what they say!

So, thanks again love for comforting me again.

Due to the fact once upon a time I went to the wrong door in life, but since you came Holy Spirit, my heart was pounding like fire when it rains in the daytime. I see heaven like golden fire in the midst of the throne God.

Well it's time for me to go to my next journey and I'm asking you Holy Spirit to guide my steps as I leave the library today, Wednesday December 3, 2014. It's going on 2:20PM.

IT'S A STRUGGLE...

It's a struggle out there, young man. It's a strong hold out there! There are too many battles in your mind out there. It's so much happening out there. Oh, don't cry out there, for you can make it as long as you don't quit on God out there. It's going to be alright young man! We know its tough times out there. So much violence in the world out there. People killing each other and it's a war zone out there.

Just find God young man even if you're facing critical issues young man, for the evil out there is not to take you down. Put your trust in God young man and follow the journey along the stairs and your faith will guide you there young man.

Whatever you do, don't step off the stairs young man, for there is a path to find and the long is the journey mate! So, remember, you're not alone, ok?

You have so much work to do in the earth and we know it's rough to be strong in a cold dark world out there.

So young man, just understand the faith that you have and the walk inside your spirit follow the path that leads to the peace you need find, just don't turn back away from this purpose. Way up the stairs, it's a key to your destiny. So yes, young man, and hey it's good for you to help those who will follow the path as well, but everyone has a path youngster. As long as you see the vision and believe the right route, I'm telling you, you're able to meet God according to your faith.

So, prepare to meet God on the right moment, endure the journey of your faith. I quite understand, it's a struggle for all, but keeping the faith is one key we can focus on. Keep the wisdom, take the walk up this stairway and don't turn back, for there is a word called "prepare to meet God."

REPENTANCE

Repentance while being misunderstood. Why so much pain in my mind?

Facing the battles in my dreams last night, I know I did leave God before, but it doesn't have to be this way. Yes, I am the apple of his eye, but sometimes in my life, I really didn't know why, why so many struggles that I had to face for myself?

Why I am misunderstood, about the wars in life? Why can't things be better than what it looks? I know I never ask to go to battles spiritually, but hey I am a man.

Going through the hardness in my thoughts, for I see someone. Does He have a purpose for me in this life? Shoot I could have given up right then and there, but He still has His hand on me, especially when I didn't understand why. Yes, I was misunderstood, about some stuff in life.
Hey, everyone has the pain they felt, but they don't see the pain in God eyes and how He feels.

WHY GOD?

How come this purpose seems so hard to live by? While walking I thought it would be nice to fly.

I see that I am in the test of my life. No need for wings for me, I have faith again, and believe. Could it be that I am seeing another testimony, inside me to see?

Across my path it appears that I have been in so much sin when leaving you before.

Being misunderstood in my own errors and ego without understanding the life that looks critical at times! I see now on my way to have faith. I understand I had to come back home again from being misunderstood and take the blindness off my mind to see clearly in my eyes.

So, you found me now! Faith is the way to draw myself walking towards you. All I can do is learn to go hard after you after all this time, Dear God.

So yes, I repent right now more than nine times.

I was the one who had been in the wild sin life. The face of a man that looked like, he was lost.

But he got heart to understand another part of him is godly sorry, like rain pouring from the skies!

REPENTENCE

Like that young man felt love by fire from the writing of this letter, God in his eyes. Repentance is my key to understanding the Kingdom, so now, I'm not misunderstood, but with understanding, I see Destiny.

SHADOW WIND BLOWS...

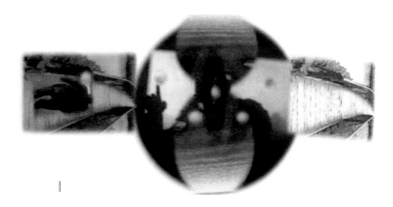

The shadow wind is blowing, the water is moving, the rocks are still, and the wind is deep...

As I walk along this journey the wind shivers my back and gives me goose bumps.

In the middle of wisdom land, trying to reach the promise. In my vision, oh know what that noise is up ahead. Sounds like a deep river pushing and the bridge that started to shake.

Oh boy! I hope I make it to the promise land indeed, for I came from a farm country. And I have nowhere else to turn but this straight and narrow path. The rocks were so steady while I am walking. This way... could it be the straight way to lead to another destiny or is this just a sign of the time?

What is going on in the midst of me? When I think of a mystery there is someone who withholds the key to find the wisdom tree.

The bridge is moving even while I am walking, but someone is moving that I can't see. The wind is blowing right through me I feel a presence that is so quietly. And the shadow of silence is focusing, and the water is pressing towards me like a ball of light flashes before my eyes. Something else is trying to distract me from the promise, but I will not turn back because I will fail my mission.

In this walk, so I much look straight, for the wind is humble, the rock is still, and the waters are slowly moving. The hidden shadow is waiting to show me the directions, while the water moves me and the rock is looking straight at me while I walk this straight pathway, because one day I did fail...

But someone I can't see was picking me off the ground, when the wind startled me. I see the shadow is a journey when the rock moved me. I have a deep place to go to while the wind is blowing through my soul. Truly there is another world out there that no one, not even me, has not seen but I believe. Truly the water was moving me. Sticks and stones will break the bones, but water will heal, and the wind will give you strength…the rock will give you strength. Wait a minute, I heard someone speak to me silently. Shadow Man saying: "Hey go along this straight path God will guide you the rest of the way."

SILENT VOICE IN THE FOREST

A silent voice I've heard, rumbling in the forest who could it be! For I'm searching for someone that I really need. Hello Confidence, where are you? Hello! Is anybody there? What's going on? Why do I hear things? I believe I am in the midst of someone, or something is in the forest trying to build a ROOT in between! Who could it be in the land of destiny? Who could it be in the deepest of my thoughts? Why is my heart feeling like thundering in my sleep as I awaken now?

Until I heard some deep sound moving; where is this noise coming from? While I'm thinking about Confidence, does the forest know the truth about its root? As I see that someone is watching me, as I take my time to understand.

What kind of plan this could be? What a long way from home, from those stairs. What a strong voice in the midst of my heart. I can't explain who is tugging in my heart and moving. My mind sounds like the forest, understand how deep is the One is moving inside. Has anyone got a clue of who is watching? No matter where I go, the voice never stops. And no matter what, if I hide behind this forest, though art there as I make some moves. You are understanding, before I make the first step, so it's a must that I learn to walk my way up again, without doubt inside. For there is one voice that I hear so humbly through my eyes and my ears. I feel the breeze from my hands to my toes. I have a strong feeling this must be God! The whole time, He was there! As I take that one last step, one more time. The first step was very difficult for me to understand. Before I breathe in and out of beautiful fresh air to take the time, and just believe so I can be strong enough to take that one last step, and believe in who was inside of me the whole time through my Destiny

In the silent voice in the forest, He was calling me.

THE MESSAGE BEHIND THE DOOR

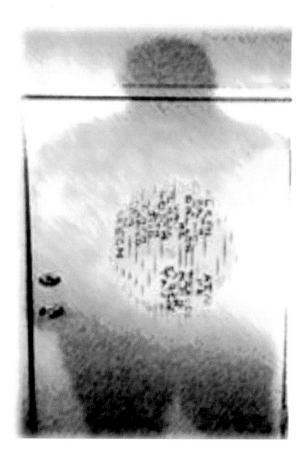

The time has changed a whole lot throughout the years of fine mystery. The world has not seen or heard the message behind the door, before my eyes.

I have seen psalms in the night!

For I have seen Heavenly sounds from the faithful sight of in my life.
I have seen God according to my faith from such a bright shine during the signs of the time.
I have not seen the invisible appearance by an outward view.

But I believe in whom I have seen from my spiritual view, for nothing from my outside is able to view the unseen, neither heard. For only in the supernatural is to believe in the impossible things.

For hey! Anything is possible with God for he works through mankind indeed. Mankind can't operate on his own. But the Father who works with in him. Hmmm…!

What a message behind the door!

Does anybody actually what this means? Has anyone heard such mystery never could be found?

Ha! Nothing can figure this out, but I believe we are enduring such psalms.

SILENT MESSAGE BEHIND THE DOOR

What a silent sound behind this door

Who is playing sounds in the center of life?

Where are these quiet words coming from?

Sounds like songs of King David. No one has seen nor heard, but all I can say is that the times are really changing. The old is gone and the new has begun and the clouds of heaven still moving, and the stars of light will fall some day at the coming of who will return. For we never understand times and seasons but understand that faith and believing are the key to every door and faith takes over once you agree with the message at the door.

Understand songs from this door and you will begin to know that you're not just the person behind the door.

The message said to me, for this was psalms indeed, in the center of my window the sound reveals, messages, saying. "You're the instrument of joy oh my soul."

For ones who reads will feel the music sounds of faith, inner belief-the peace that lies within.
I hear an angel say to me silently, "Be aware to entertain angels unaware".

Heaven send me a
Message Behind the Door.

THE QUIET WILDERNESS

The quiet wilderness I see a sound in the clouds and a soft melody sound in the forest.

Who could it be making such a quiet sound in my century?

Who could it be making my heartbeat like the trees that have strengthened my ability?

WHO AM I to be a little king in the forest?

I saw beautiful standing in the center of my eye. I never thought I could be alive after all the struggling. I never understood who I was before. I never thought I could be in the light after all the darkness I have faced from a cold, wavering night! I was lost in the woods. Who can find me and what is that sound that's in the skies between? Is it God who is pulling on me?

In a time like this, I once was lost, but now I am found. I was blind but now I see. There is a quiet voice in the wilderness calling me. No matter what life brings, if I ever fall, I will make sure I stand again.

This battle in my head was not for weakness, but it's for my strength.

We can accomplish and succeed as long as we believe in the One who is between the clouds indeed. I didn't understand God much in my life, but I understand Him in the way I am being still. Just focus above my misery and take the time to believe in this mystery about me.

Even though I am not noticed by some people, it's because I am in the wilderness being developed. And go on a journey to another century, I am history and never have to be discouraged about this. For I will conquer whatever I miss in my life, for I will make it through this battle inside me.

For the things I am going through is a test for me, so I will take the time to believe that whoever is truly with me, He is truly quiet and standing above me and watching me every time. And will catch me when I fail, but this time I will not let my heart stumble. In this, my spirit is quietness.

FREEDOM FROM SLAVERY

The souls proclaim freedom for all the hearts crying out. The bondage shall be broken the poverty must be broken, the starvation must be filled with food, the hungry shall be fed and the spirit shall feel free.

No chains with no questions towards my freedom. No one shall be bound by the traditional ways.

No one shall allow money or materialistic things to cause yourself to be bound by the system. No evil and no sin shall not put you to a place of prison in the brain. We are not forgotten by God. We are not under any systems, unless you're trapped in the system, and don't know the way to be free.

Try faith and understand your inner self of your identity to be free. You're in heritage is free. Fear is broken from how you carry your freedom in life. Be culture free and not bound in your freedom land.

Because any culture has a right to their freedom, for our slavery ways was not fear for us, but allowed us to be stronger than our slavery feeling. It's either we feel the freedom for all, or we feel bound by the society. We are not bound by money or anything, but we are bound for Heaven for Kingdom is eternity.

No matter what, we have freedom to establish in the power of the free mind, and a free mind is the wisdom to sustain and to proclaim. Our liberty is empowered by God only, and not our luxuries.

There is no freedom in chains or in our money. Wisdom is greater than our wealth. We have no masters, unless you desire who your master to be. The believers understand freedom so may all remember to be free for all. The gold has no breath to breathe in your thoughts, but your wisdom spirit is better than the mansions you see. Your vision is forever in life of how you think, speaking life is how you think. No death can hold you down. Your spirit uplifts you. No chains for human beings.

Either we chose light or the dark, it's a choice in life. I will never forget my brother Errol Layne, a man of God, who said "We are free in Christ indeed and we must choose God or the devil".

This is so true. I believe anyone who is creative in the image of the Father must take the time to understand who they are and not what they can do, either we can rule over evil or we can be bound and not feel free. Hey, a free spirit is the wisdom to think in the free mind and having a free mind is the heart of freedom.

Yes Mon, I love you Jamaica for I'm looking forward to seeing you soon.

WARS AND RUMORS OF WAR

(Inspired by Matthew 24:6)

The War Rumors of Wars ROAR! In the jungle wars! In the cities Roar! In the valleys, wars!

So much happening on planet earth! It's time to overcome these carnalities! HERE I ROAR! In the wilderness I see battles in the worlds. What is going on here? Why does this exist and why are people fighting over lands?

ROAR!

In the earth we shall not quit! In this battle of our lives, it's time to face our own battles that try to defeat our minds. Stop fighting amongst ourselves. There is another battle. This is deeper than our outer limits!

ROAR!

It's a battle in the spiritual, roaming in the brain cells where you have to face the enemy who will cause You to fear or get weak in whatever battle you're facing. These battles are based on kingdom against kingdom and lands against land. But the battle is not yours...

Hear me ROAR!

This battle belongs to the Lord. DO you understand soldier? I know you're facing serious depression, but you can't give up on the purpose that the Lord has for you! Oh darn it! Please think first before you take a second thought. First you need to have a plan. Study the ground first. From within your inner man, the spirit is part of you, and this is not just some physical thing. For goodness sake! It's just like overcoming the pressure inside the mind! Just don't give your strength to the wrong spirit but give it to the Lord who made you and don't give yourself to the wrong stuff that will hinder your walls. Just always take the time to protect your ground and study them before reaching the other level! This is a war zone for real!

Who are you fighting and what are you're fighting over? I'll say the best fight you can ever do is fight the good fight of faith in this mission, because the weapons were not for a carnal appetite, but it's up to you to be mighty through God to the pulling down strong hold fears that will grip you to pieces.

Check this out soldier! You will win the victory through Christ who is the strength in you in this warfare!

If you come short, pick up where you got distracted and start accomplishing it! By speaking life over your inner walls, it's ok to challenge yourself, to help strengthen you. Use wisdom at war. In the realm of the spirit, not by the works of rumors, of a human being lifestyle, just basic training your life in learning.

Have a humble spirit soldiers, we Peoples! Our Lord will save us from terror in this planet! Stay in the faith.

WISDOM TREE IN ANOTHER ELEMENT

WAIT A MINUTE!

It appears that Wisdom Tree is not on planet earth, so now I have to leave from here and find it!

O Lord Help me with this next traveling mission!

I see I have to leave now. It's 7:00 pm…could be 00:7.

Oh boy! I have to move quickly by my faith now!

Well, I have to go now, and I will find you Wisdom Tree. No doubt in my mind…I will find you!

May God help a soldier like me through this mission. Well, from back to the future right?

Ok there is a little way to go, but I will get to this element for sure.

Ok time to go with God as He guides my feet!

For Mr. Bookman will trust in the Lord indeed!

TRANSPORT INSIDE WISDOM LOCATION

What is happening to me? Why am I being attacked every time I'm striving, to aim towards wisdom?

What is going on? Every time I keep a straight path, I begin to see something is trying to hurt me!

Why is evil trying to distract me? And why is this struggle so strong before me?

What can I do to get the wisdom I need to accomplish my mission? Who is attacking my thoughts as I am led to go?

This straight path, O Lord, why allow me to struggle in this area? Why bring me in the wilderness in this journey?

HELLO! Is anybody out there?

Is anyone caring for my soul, even if I fail!

HELLO! Does anyone hear me out there?

Why am I alone being wrestled by some evil forces?

Who is this and why have you come to take me out even when I stand? OH NO YOU DON'T!

You evil forces I will defeat you! I will defend my destiny! Where God will guide me.

I know I've got to be in a serious test and trial of my life in this way! I will stand in my struggles today. even if this my last day! It doesn't matter how hard I fight, I will not beat the air, but I will stand while being tackled by this demon! I will not let myself down! NO WAY! Demon of darkness I will not let you beat me!

For my God is still with me, the report of the Lord is still with me and He will transport me to Wisdom Tree, and I will not let this struggle take my thoughts! OH NO WAY! So, if I have to fight, I will win! If I have to struggle, I will struggle! If this is my last straw, for I believe in God and I know this is a challenge for me again. So not this time devil! For I am not going to turn my back on God. So even if you try to pull on me and cause me to fear you, I will not fear you because my Lord has my heart still! You can't have my heart and you can't take my soul. I will fight my way through this here, and not turn my back!

I know who I belong to and His name is Alpha and Omega; the beginning and the ending. And that name is Christ the Lord. So, I will not let the enemy rip me or break me because I will be transported to Wisdom Tree.

Ok I see the trial was only a test, so I will keep straight! I will keep straight! I will because Yes, I CAN!

UNDEFILED LIFE

Poem movie based on a true story: Leaving my undefiled restless life

So, it's been a long time for me to the point I can't even describe myself
Facing trouble in my mind.
Could I be stressed out from such a terrible relationship?
Restless nights with no love music inside!
Darn! Why in the world I get myself caught in and out of bad vibes?
Or should I say…the wrong relationships…into undefiled distractions!
Make me feel like I lost my way
To the point I can't even see the day, until a change begins with me.

I can't think crazy. OK, But I can say this…

I need to be released from the reality that really discourages me! Oh God, why I had to be alone again, for in my life, seems single since I was involved in a serious relationship in time past, yeah that's right truly this was my past life.

Dang! Even some women who were in mine, we experienced the immaturity and never really understood each other, but the interesting bedtime story ends up as a broken record player! Screaming out of my lungs! I can't take these issues to my house anymore.

These problems have to leave, for real, and I'm not playing here! Don't you understand?

Ladies who prayed for a good man, only and not really seeing the struggles he faced, but a perfect man is what she looks into, especially while men prayed for Mrs. Right in their lives.

In the same way, asking God for over decades and still searching for the same love when you can't notice the change. Here is the truth: Men and women have a struggle, it's just a test of our faith. Step up and get out of undefiled.

Start getting back into place, in shape, thinking straight!

Don't leave God if you're not balanced yet! Look, it doesn't matter who leaves you, just know God is still available and He will bring someone special for you; to love you and treat you right as well you treat that person right.

Listen it's not the money, you're carried away. Wow! She thought I wasn't even thinking straight. Even if I didn't buy a lamp in the room, dang! But every purpose is nothing new under the sun. But the dark room sure can make some attention as well, seeing new colors of the actions of how we mistreat one another. Wow! I'm like really tripped out right now!

What's the point? Who is missing in my life? I guess it was me.

Away from old ways, focus on new way of living. Hey, understand my quote; you see the person you think you are, but those past days are over, for the new days are up ahead and your mind has just been wondering.

But now you're uplifting…
taking off the stress...
have some gratitude…
clearing up your attitude…
and smile you're graduating from college soon.

Feel the motion of the picture bearing my undefiled, in the way ground was my single thoughts.

WHEN THE STRUGGLE IS OVER

When the struggle is over, I will stand still,
When the struggle is over, I will balance my feet again!
When the struggle is over, I don't have to feel down about it!
For I can gain the power in me again.

I see God still has His people's back. Shoot! I know that even the devil could not even stand.

For my faith is still activated, I don't even have to feel faded, only God blesses us to even make it!

I have no time to waste this, so I can say we are predestinated by grace.

I'm not Mr. self-righteous in my struggle OK?!

We all have them of course, and every struggle has a purpose, different from another.

But we still have to be strong again, over the way we think. Understand the missions, still repeat

Wow! I'm in the wilderness thinking about facing destiny. Could there be eyes in the tree looking at me?

While standing in the forest seeking, thank God I'm still alive from all the hell I went through!

I know what it's like to be weak and understand what it's like to be sick in my mind! What a REHAB!

Moment of time, tick tock! Tick tock! Who in the world is bringing sounds in my ears? I hear birds like a lion in the skies, while the struggle is being separated from my eyes,

So, no matter how I see struggles, I don't have to be angry about obstacles or get mad at God.

But I am willing to crack a smile and be worthy to raise my hands again and hey live the American dream!

By standing up the flag again. Because the future has no end, but the struggles will soon be over until

The daytime is done…

WHEN THE STRUGGLE IS OVER

DE' ANO DISCOVERED GOD

It was the last moment of time facing the end of 3,000 BC years ago. Seeing the past was the reflection of power

Looking towards the hills of His Interesting Power; so much flame in the center of the water.

Too much ice in the winter, so much rain in the summer too many rocks in the midst of trees,

Hearing deep voices from Heaven deeply; silence my knees!

Hearing the voice of thunder in the inner most part of my feelings, the skies started awaking.

In my eyes, everything was calm and the fire started speaking; the day the flames began to blaze waves

Sounding God in the mystery of the ancient days.

As a detective of this understanding of the past was acquainted towards me for some reason.

I have come along way home from the City and seeing the history in the past was like a map in my sleep that the past from 3,000 years was true.

The day God truly was speaking.

GOD'S GRANDMOTHER

God's Grand mother one of the mother's who always has a way to bring the family together.

God's grand mother someone who is God-fearing, not afraid of the storm;

that comes across by the way side to pick up all God's children! Oh grand mother dear;

How often do you keep all God's children together. For so many years you prayed

For all people your are a century of one special ansestors just like the rest of our elders.

with perfection in our history.

The one who is strong indeed, that succeed through the mission.

Even while cooking soul food for all God's children.

You sure take the time to cook home made hot cakes, and cooking a hot warm Sunday dinner!

And if the children act up, you still give that old fashion old school whip.

But through it all! Grandmother; you will always be inspiring,

Towards us in our hearts by the love you carry; like Martin Luther king said along time ago.

I have A DREAM! We will all come together again

Cedric De'ano Harris.

WARS ON HUMAN SOCIETY

The Human society are very potential in understanding about what's really happening in the world.

And everyone is screaming and angry about this whole terror that is going on! Speak on human rights.

And government laws, we are very react on what we are facing in our system today and not that many people are happy with new laws and the world is getting worse than Pearl Harbor.

So many people can react to what is going on in the world the beginning of new world order has started.

And the confusion is here in our country today the world war three is set in place. These issues are not very good at all but if only everyone pull together stick with their faith and everything would be a great humanity with the power of respect that will help change the world Respect is what a person can do for you and never receive nothing in materialistic things. Turn away wars and find a peace of mind.

(A peace of mind) is wiser than a person holding a gun having the mind out of control loaded with egos.

War rumors of wars on terror and money problems and oil gas and weapons on our turf and other countries what is the government really doing because he sure is changing these new laws that are not

The truth just like you take one dollar bill and rip it in pieces would it be a puzzle only you can search that out because every money comes with a code a change of new orders concerning. But money is not the issue

It's a mental disorderly conduct that hits the conscious of the mind. Like who are we feeding are we being fed by fools or wise counseling who bring us knowledge and wisdom with understanding.

All nations are at estate and Israel is trouble and other countries are as well the power of confusion

Is now begun it's time for an awaking too what we are seeing with our own eye's! Are we disbelief about what's around us! Against what we believe in But the truth is money is not so much of the problem it's human brains with a whole lot is warfare and that's where the real war is the battle of those doubting life in that mind. Also Humans has Human race issues but it's all a spiritual conflict between good and evil forces. But only the wise would be wise and the fool still be a fool.

Even another war is out there far beyond human brains but we are talking about spiritual demons against angels that are soon too come forth but already set up different territories on earth that no human form can see them.

So the key is Us human beings are spirits as well in all the worlds we must stand up and be strong while the storm is getting even deeper. Until then we have choices to make concerning speaking life or death is in the power of the tongue.

Why argue with one another over politicians and laws and governments and religious belief

But in everything must be specific' on how can we solve this issue' It's called Bring humanity together.

The good news is we still have our being as a people on the planet earth has a decision to make for ourselves and being good by reason on facts about these changes and the laws that are not truth but find God is the key and seek His interesting truth.

A Message from Cedric...

Greetings

Life...it's been a rocky road for me, and I did not realize how much gift and talent that I actually have, now becoming a first-time author in spite of suffering through mental illness, having to have my spiritual mother and the rest of my family and friends pray for my recovery. Between times, I begin to write in my notebook by the water when I moved to Virginia, where I now call "home".

My book is basically an adventure in biblical energy and time. The book of poems was inside my heart each time I listened within and entered a quiet moment. In those times, I began to write like I could actually look and see something, I would then write something deep and passionate. My vision for this book is that it be like a movie book of poems to those who love to read cool stories and perhaps like to imagine the idea of the story that they are reading. So, in this story, I guess you can consider me as the director in this fantastic film story but in poetry format; "The mystery book of Poems".

I am thankful for the love of family and friends in various times of my life, especially those I've suffered through on the dark road of life. So, I decided to make a change and still striving towards perfection, and now any time negative energy hits me, I begin to think thoughts of "Success".

So, as you begin to ready these books of poems, I pray you will be encouraged and remember nobody is perfect we all strive perfection in God's earth!

And like they say on the streets "it's the King upstairs".

ABOUT THE AUTHOR

"Born in Virginia, raised in Houston, TX, Cedric Harris has experienced many challenges and struggles in his life, but has overcome them all. He is a Believer in Christ who is grateful to God for helping him gain victory in many areas of his life. Cedric loves his family, cherishes his friends, and when writing, he desires to tell a story through his poems that will take the reader on a journey through the Word of God in a unique manner. His prayer is that through his poetry, the reader will be encouraged and remember that no one is perfect, but that we are all striving for perfection in God's earth."

Book Author
Cedric Harris
to

Wendy

Made in the USA
Middletown, DE
01 December 2021

53913940R00058